CW00405650

CHESTER'S EASIEST
SONGS OF THE BRITISH ISLES

arranged by Carol Barratt

For Catharine Evans

ENGLAND

SCOTLAND

WALES

IRELAND

The chord symbols suggested have been chosen to suit the solo melody and
do not always correspond with the harmony of the arrangements, as importance has
been placed on interesting left hand accompaniments using simple hand positions.

This book © Copyright 1993 Chester Music
Order No.CH60806. ISBN 0-7119-3255-7

Illustrations by Sarah Lenton
Music processed by Barnes Music Engraving
Printed in the United Kingdom by Caligraving Limited, Thetford, Norfolk.

Chester Music Limited
(A division of Music Sales Limited)

DRINK TO ME ONLY

2. I sent thee late a rosy wreath,
   Not so much honouring thee,
   As giving it a hope that there
   It could not wither 'd be,
   But thou thereon didst only breathe,
   And send'st it back to me,
   Since when it grows, and smells, I swear,
   Not of itself, but thee.

ALL THROUGH THE NIGHT

Welsh

Sleep, my love, and peace at-tend thee, All through the night;

Guar - dian an - gels God will lend thee, All through the night;

Soft the drow - sy hours are creep - ing, Hill and dale in slum - ber sleep - ing,

I my lov - ing vi - gil keep - ing, All through the night.

2.   Angels watching ever round thee,
All through the night;
In thy slumbers close surround thee,
All through the night.
They should of all fears disarm thee,
No forebodings should alarm thee,
They will let no peril harm thee,
All through the night.

THE HARP THAT ONCE

Irish

The harp that once through Ta - ra's Halls, Its soul of mu - sic shed, Now
hangs as mute on Ta - ra's walls, As if that soul were fled. So
sleeps the pride of for - mer days, So glo - ry's thrill is o'er; And
hearts that once beat high for praise, Now feel that pulse no more.

2.   No more to chiefs and ladies bright
The harp of Tara swells;
The chord alone, that breaks the night,
Its tale of ruin tells.
Thus Freedom now so seldom wakes,
The only throb she gives
Is when some heart indignant breaks
To show that still she lives.

THE GYPSY LADDIE

2. The lady she cam' doon the stair
   Her maidens twa afore her O;
   But when they spied her weel-faured face,
   They cast their spells oot o'er her O.

3. Lord Castles he cam' hame at e'en,
   Enquiring for his lady O;
   "The hounds is run and the hawk is flown
   And the gypsy's awa' wi' your lady O."

4. "Come saddle me to the black, the black
   Mak' haste and soon be ready O;
   For it's meat and drink I winna taste,
   Till I get back my lady O."

5. They've rode east and they've rode wes
   Till them cam' to yonder boggie O;
   And there they spied the weel-faured
        maid,
   Wi' the gypsies a' standin' roond her O.

6. "Will ye gang wi' me, my honey and my
        heart,
   Will ye gang wi' me, my lady O;
   And I swear by the sword that hangs by
        my side,
   The black band shall never steal thee O."

7. "I winna come wi' you, my honey and m
        heart,
   I winna come wi' you, my dearie O;
   Till I hae drunk the breest I brewed,
   And that's in the water o' Eerie O."

6

SCARBOROUGH FAIR

English

Are you go - ing to Scar - bor - ough Fair?

Pars - ley, sage, rose - mar - y and thyme. Re -

- mem - ber me to one who lives there.

She once was a true love of mine.

2. Have her make me a cambric shirt.
   Parsley, sage, rosemary and thyme.
   Without a seam or fine needle work.
   Then she'll be a true love of mine.

3. Have her wash it in yonder dry well.
   Parsley, sage, rosemary and thyme.
   Where ne'er a drop of water e'er fell.
   Then she'll be a true love of mine.

4. If she tells me she can't I'll reply
   Parsley, sage, rosemary and thyme.
   And let me know that at least she will try.
   Then she'll be a true love of mine.

COCKLES AND MUSSELS

Irish

In Dub-lin's fair ci-ty, where girls are so pret-ty, I
G   Em   C6   D7

first set my eyes on sweet Mol-ly Ma-lone, As she
G   Em   A7   D7

wheeled her wheel-bar-row through streets broad and nar-row, Cry-ing
G   Em   C6   D7

Chorus

"Cock-les and mus-sels a-live, a-live O!" "A-
G   C/G   G   Am   G/D   D7   G   D7

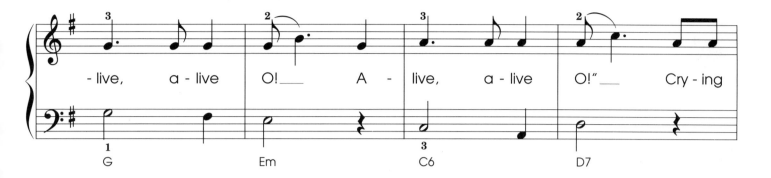

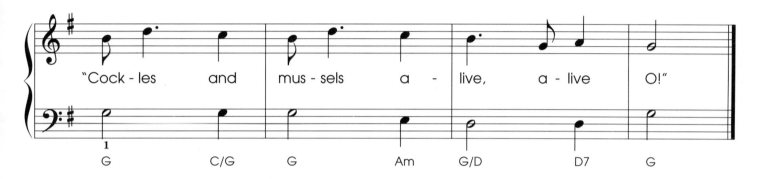

2. She was a fishmonger, but sure 'twas no wonder,
   For so were her father and mother before;
   And they each wheeled their barrow through streets broad and narrow,
   Crying "Cockles and mussels alive, alive O!"

   Chorus "Alive, alive O!. . . . . . ."

3. She died of a fever, and no one could save her,
   And that was the end of sweet Molly Malone;
   Her ghost wheels her barrow through streets broad and narrow,
   Crying "Cockles and mussels alive, alive O!"

   Chorus "Alive, alive O!. . . . . . ."

DAVID OF THE WHITE ROCK

2. Last night I heard an angel thus say,
"David, fly home on the wings of thy lay."
Harp of my youth, and thy music, adieu,
Widow and children, God's blessing on you.

BARBARA ALLEN

English

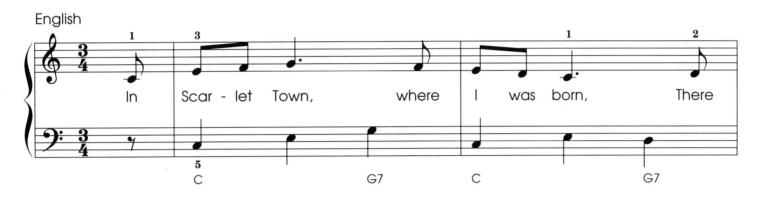

In Scar - let Town, where I was born, There

C   G7   C   G7

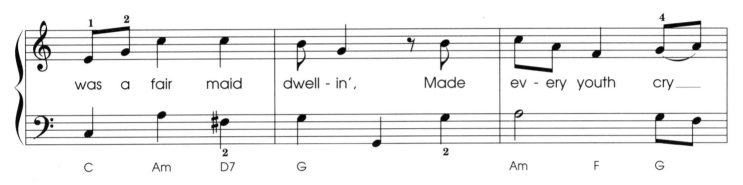

was a fair maid dwell - in', Made ev - ery youth cry___

C   Am   D7   G   Am   F   G

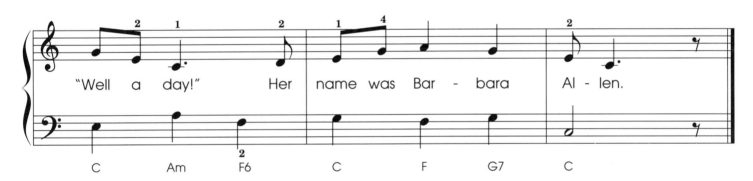

"Well a day!" Her name was Bar - bara Al - len.

C   Am   F6   C   F   G7   C

2. All in the merry month of May,
   When green buds they were swellin';
   Young Jemmy Grove on his death-bed lay,
   For love of Barbara Allen.

3. So slowly, slowly, she came up,
   And slowly she came nigh him;
   And all she said, when there she came,
   "Young man, I think you're dying.'

4. He turned his face unto the wall,
   As deadly pangs he fell in:
   "Adieu! Adieu! Adieu to you all,
   Adieu to Barbara Allen."

5. When he was dead, and laid in grave,
   Her heart was struck with sorrow,
   "O mother, mother, make my bed,
   For I shall die tomorrow."

6. She, on her death-bed as she lay,
   Begg'd to be buried by him;
   And sore repented of her day,
   That she did e'er deny him.

WILL YE NO COME BACK AGAIN

Scottish

Bon - nie Char - lie's now a - wa', Safe - ly owre the friend - ly main;

Mo-ny a heart will break in twa, Should he ne'er come back a-gain.

Chorus

Will ye no come back a-gain? Will ye no come back_ a-gain?

Bet - ter lo'ed ye can-na be, Will ye no come back a-gain?

* Try adding the B♮ ♪ to make it sound more "Scottish".

2.   English bribes were a' in vain,
       Tho' puir, an puirer, we maun be:
       Siller canna buy the heart
       That beats aye for thine and thee.
       Chorus: Will ye no. . . . .

3.   We watch'd thee in the gloaming hour,
       We watch'd thee in the morning grey;
       Tho' thirty thousand pounds they gie
       There is nane that wad betray.
       Chorus: Will ye no. . . . .

4.   Sweet's the lavelock's note and lang,
       Lilting wildly up the glen:
       But aye to me he sings ae sang:
       "Will ye no come back again?"
       Chorus: Will ye no. . . . .

BLOW AWAY THE MORNING DEW

English

Up - on the sweet - est sum - mer time In the mid - dle of the morn, A

pret - ty dam - sel I es - pied, The fair - est ev - er born. And sing

blow a - way the morn - ing dew, The dew and the dew.

Blow a - way the morn - ing dew, How sweet the winds do blow.

2. She gathered up her lovely flowers
   And spent her time in sport,
   As if in pretty Cupid's bowers
   She daily did resort.
   Chorus: And sing. . . .

3. The yellow cowslip by the brim,
   The daffodil as well,
   The timid primrose, pale and trim,
   The pretty snow-drop bell.
   Chorus: And sing. . . .

4. She's gone with all those flowers sweet
   Of white, of red, of blue,
   And unto me, about my feet,
   Is only left the rue.
   Chorus: And sing. . . .

THE ASH GROVE

Welsh

Down yon - der green_ val - ley where stream - lets_ me - an - der, When

G   D7   G   C6   A   D

twi - light_ is___ fad - ing, I pen - sive - ly rove; Or

G   C   G/D   D7   G

at the bright_ noon - tide in sol - i - tude_ wan - der A -

G   D7   G   C6   A   D

- mid the_ dark_ shades of the lone - ly Ash Grove; 'Twas_

G   C   G/D   D7   G

there, while_ the_ black - bird was cheer - ful - ly_ sing - ing, I

G   E7   Am   D7

14

2. Still glows the bright sunshine o'er valley and mountain,
    Still warbles the blackbird its note from the tree;
    Still trembles the moonbeam on streamlet and fountain,
    But what are the beauties of nature to me?
    With sorrow, deep sorrow, my bosom is laden,
    All day I go mourning in search of my love;
    Ye echoes! Oh tell me, where is the sweet maiden?
    "She sleeps 'neath the green turf down by the Ash Grove."

WHEN I WAS A TAILOR

English

When_ I_____ was a tai - lor, a tai - lor, a tai - lor, When_

I_____ was a tai - lor, a tai - lor was I   It was

Chorus

this way, and that way, and this way, and that way, When___

I_____ was a tai - lor, a tai - lor was I.

2.   When I was a farmer, a farmer, a farmer,
     When I was a farmer, a farmer was I
     Chorus: It was this way. . . .

3.   When I was a baker, a baker, a baker,
     When I was a baker, a baker was I
     Chorus: It was this way. . . .

4.   When I was a miner, a miner, a miner,
     When I was a miner, a miner was I
     Chorus: It was this way. . . .

THE BLUE BELL OF SCOTLAND

2. "Oh where, and oh where did your Highland laddie dwell?
Oh where, and oh where did your Highland laddie dwell?"
"He dwelt in merry Scotland, at the sign of the Blue Bell;
And it's oh in my heart that I love my laddie well."

3. "Suppose, oh suppose that your Highland lad should die!
Suppose, oh suppose that your Highland lad should die!"
"The bagpipes should play o'er him, and I'd lay me down to cry,
But it's oh in my heart that I feel he will not die."

LAND OF MY FATHERS

Welsh

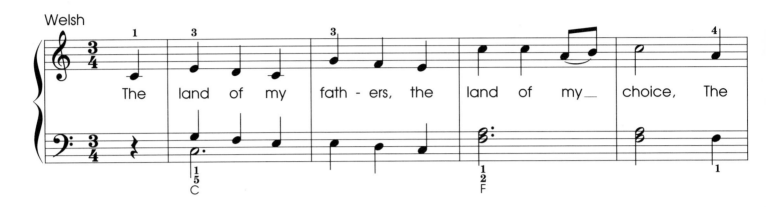

The land of my fath - ers, the land of my choice, The

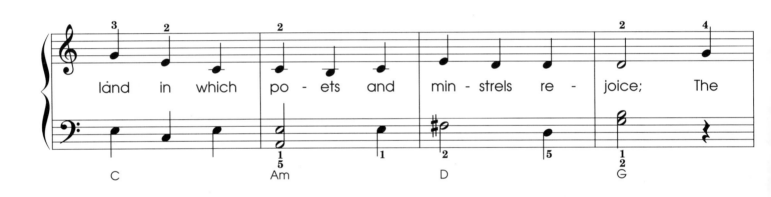

land in which po - ets and min - strels re - joice; The

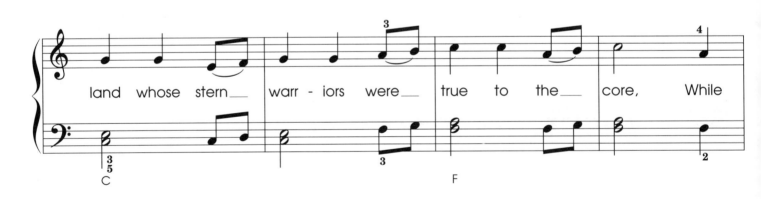

land whose stern warr - iors were true to the core, While

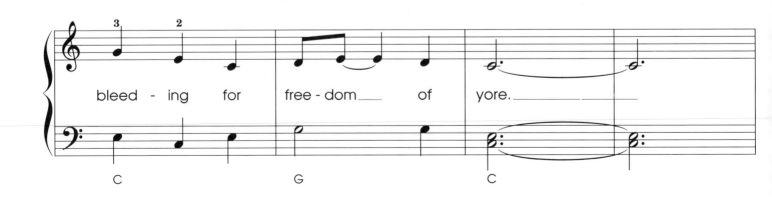

bleed - ing for free - dom of yore.

2. The mountains of Cambria, the Eden of Bards,
    Each hill and each valley, excite my regards;
    To the ears of her patriot how charming still seems
    The music that flows in her streams.
    Chorus: Wales, Wales. . . . . . .

ANNIE LAURIE

Scottish

Max - well - ton braes are bon - nie where ear - ly falls the__
C   F   C   D9

dew, And it's there that An - nie Lau - rie gave me her prom - ise
G   C   F   C   G7

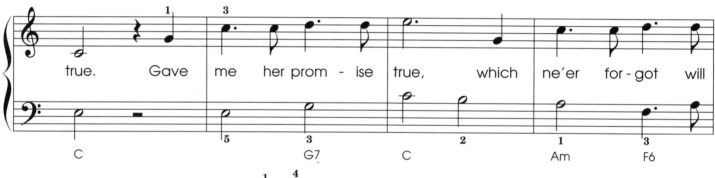

true. Gave me her prom - ise true, which ne'er for - got will
C   G7   C   Am   F6

be; And for bon - nie bon - nie An - nie Laur - ie I'd__ lay__ me doon and dee.
E   Am   F   C   Am   Fmaj7 G7   C

2.   Her brow is like the snow-drift,
      Her neck is like the swan,
      Her face it is the fairest
      That e'er the sun shone on.
      That e'er the sun shone on,
      And dark blue is her e'e;
      And for bonnie Annie Laurie
      I'd lay me doon and dee.

3.   Like dew on the gowan lying,
      Is the fa' o' her fairy feet;
      And like winds in summer sighing,
      Her voice is low and sweet.
      Her voice is low and sweet,
      And she's a' the world to me;
      And for bonnie Annie Laurie
      I'd lay me doon and dee.

EARLY ONE MORNING

2. "Oh, gay is the garland, and fresh are the roses,
   I've cull'd from the garden to bind on thy brow.
   Chorus: Oh, don't deceive me. . . ."

3. "Remember the vows that you made to your Mary,
   Remember the bow'r where you vow'd to be true.
   Chorus: Oh, don't deceive me. . . ."

4. Thus sang the poor maiden, her sorrows bewailing,
   Thus sang the poor maid in the valley below:
   Chorus: "Oh, don't deceive me. . . .

LONDONDERRY AIR

Irish

2. Acushla mine, your lips are ever smiling,
   They smiled their way into my longing heart,
   Your roguish eyes to me are so beguiling,
   I pray the saints, that never may we part.
   When winter comes, and all the world is dreary,
   And sun and stars no longer seem to shine,
   The world is dark, and I am sad and weary,
   'Tis then I need you most of all, Acushla, mine.

3. Acushla mine, when birds again are singing
   Their mating song, and all the land is gay,
   When, at the church, the wedding bells are ringing
   Mavourneen, dear, 'twill be a happy day.
   And through the years no matter what the weather,
   Around my heart, your love will still entwine,
   We'll wander on, as long as we're together,
   And wander in to Paradise, Acushla mine.

AULD LANG SYNE

Scottish

2.   And there's a hand, my trusty friend, and
gie's a hand in thine.
We'll tak' a right gude wil-ly waught, for
Auld Lang Syne.

Chorus: For Auld. . . . .